EPHESIANS 6

Coloring and Activity book

Bible verses and their application

I can be strong during difficult times because I have God's power with me.

Write inside the strokes some ways that God might help the little girl to be strong during difficult times.

"Be strong in the Lord, and in the power of His might."

God's power is like a spiritual armor that protects me from the devil's temptations.

Match the armor pieces to the correct places on the boy's body.

"Put on the whole armor of God, so that you can stand strong against the devil's plans."

I should not fight against others that might do mean things to me, but rather against the evil and the bad.

Which of these children will make the right choice?

*"We don't fight against people on earth,
but against the devil's kingdom."*

The devil is our enemy, but we can't see him or strike at him physically.

Can you find the seven differences in these pictures?
"Our fight is against the spiritual powers of evil in the world and in the heavens."

I have to get myself ready. Like a great warrior of God, I can learn how to put on a spiritual armor to protect me.

Follow the letter path, filling in the blanks as you go.

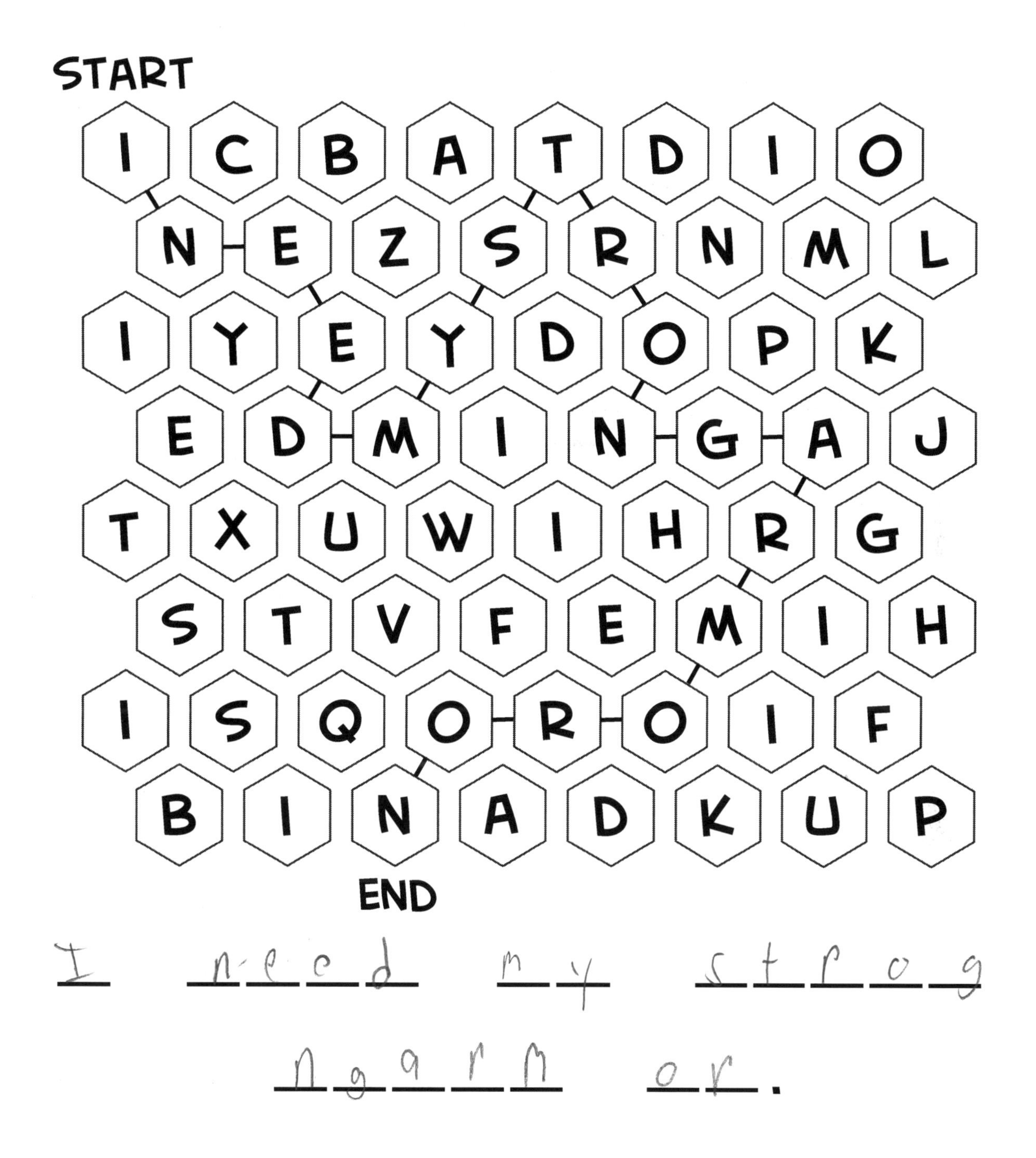

"That's why we need to put on the whole armor of God, so that we may be able to stand strong when evil comes our way."

God is strong and powerful and He is always with me. Like a good tight belt, the truth of God's Word will support and protect me.

On each belt, write something that makes you think of honesty or a word to describe honesty.

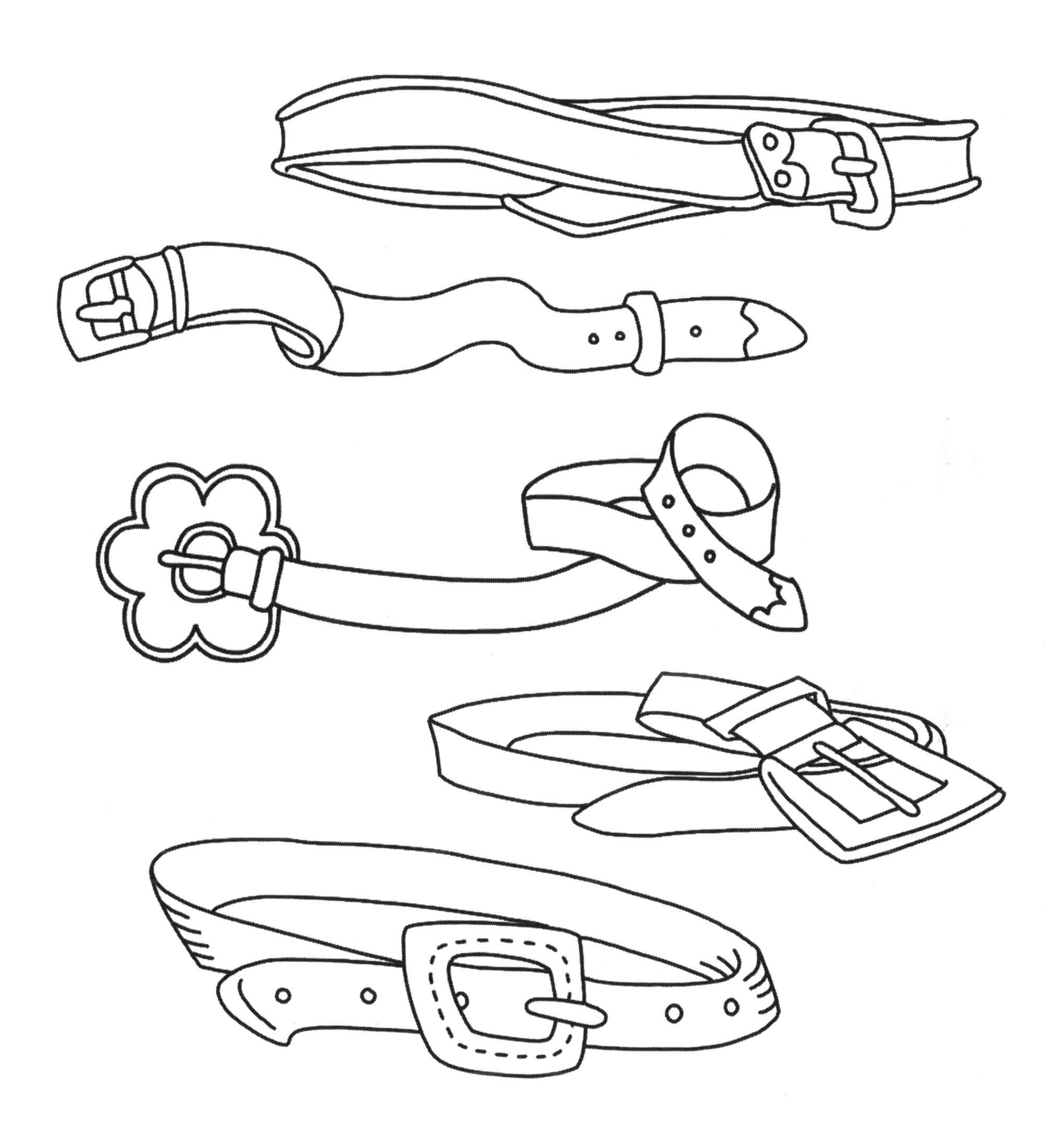

"So stand firm, having the belt of truth around your waist."

God teaches me to do what is right and to show kindness. I guard my own heart and demonstrate that with God's help I can show love to others.

Copy the words from the hearts in the right order onto the lines below.

....

....

....

"And on your chest, wear the breastplate of righteousness."

I am ready to go and tell others about the good news of God's love and peace.

Draw a line from one boot to the other in order to make a matching pair.

"And on your feet, prepare yourself to walk and spread the good news of peace."

I use the shield of faith to protect myself from the devil! Faith is to trust God and believe in Him, even though I can't see Him with my eyes.

Draw the unfinished half of the shield,
copying symmetrically from the left side.

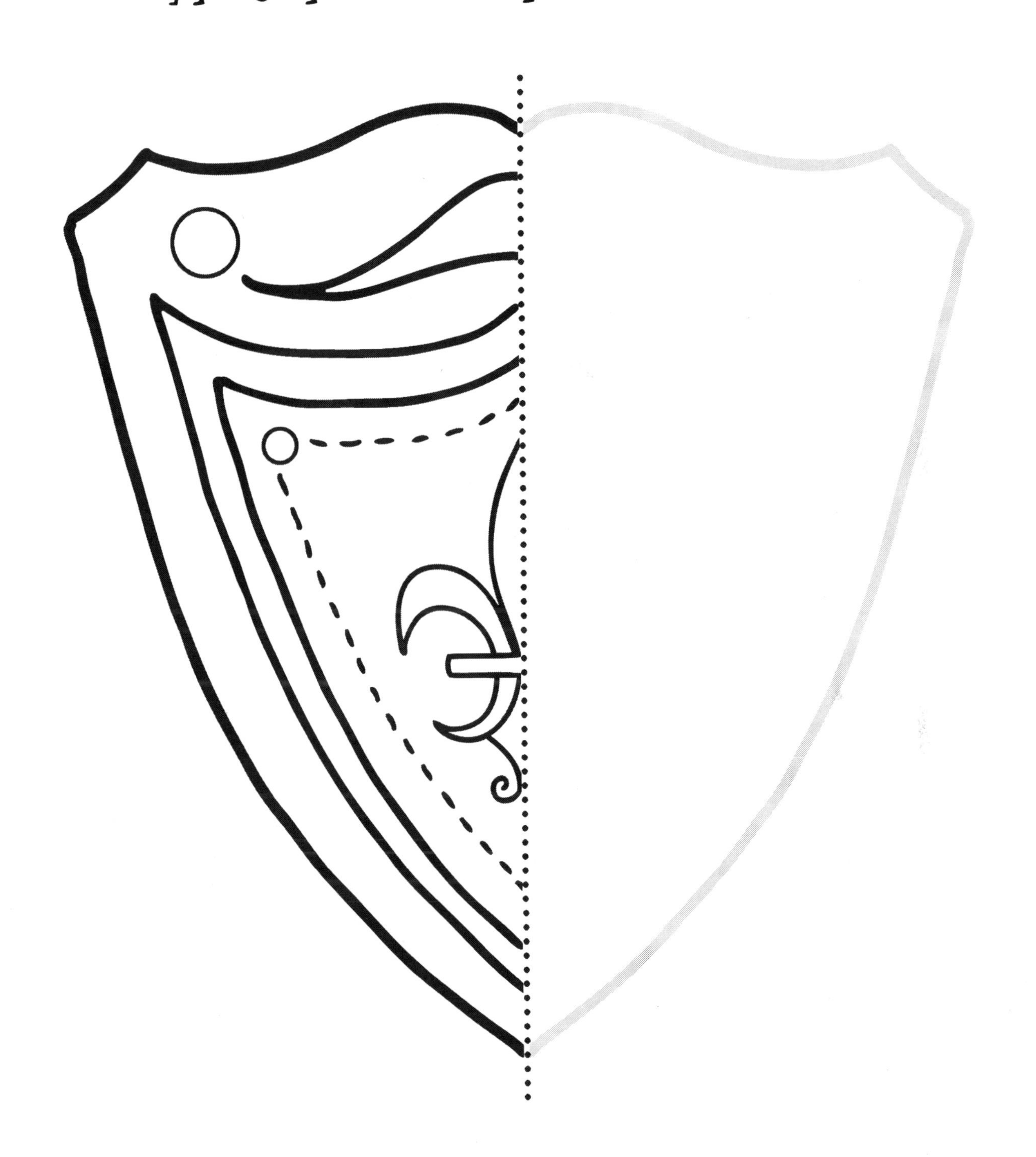

"By taking the shield of faith, you will be able to put out all the fiery darts of the wicked."

Jesus' sacrifice protects my soul in the same way that a helmet protects my head. God rescued me from my mistakes when Jesus died to save me.

Follow the numbers and dots to finish the picture.

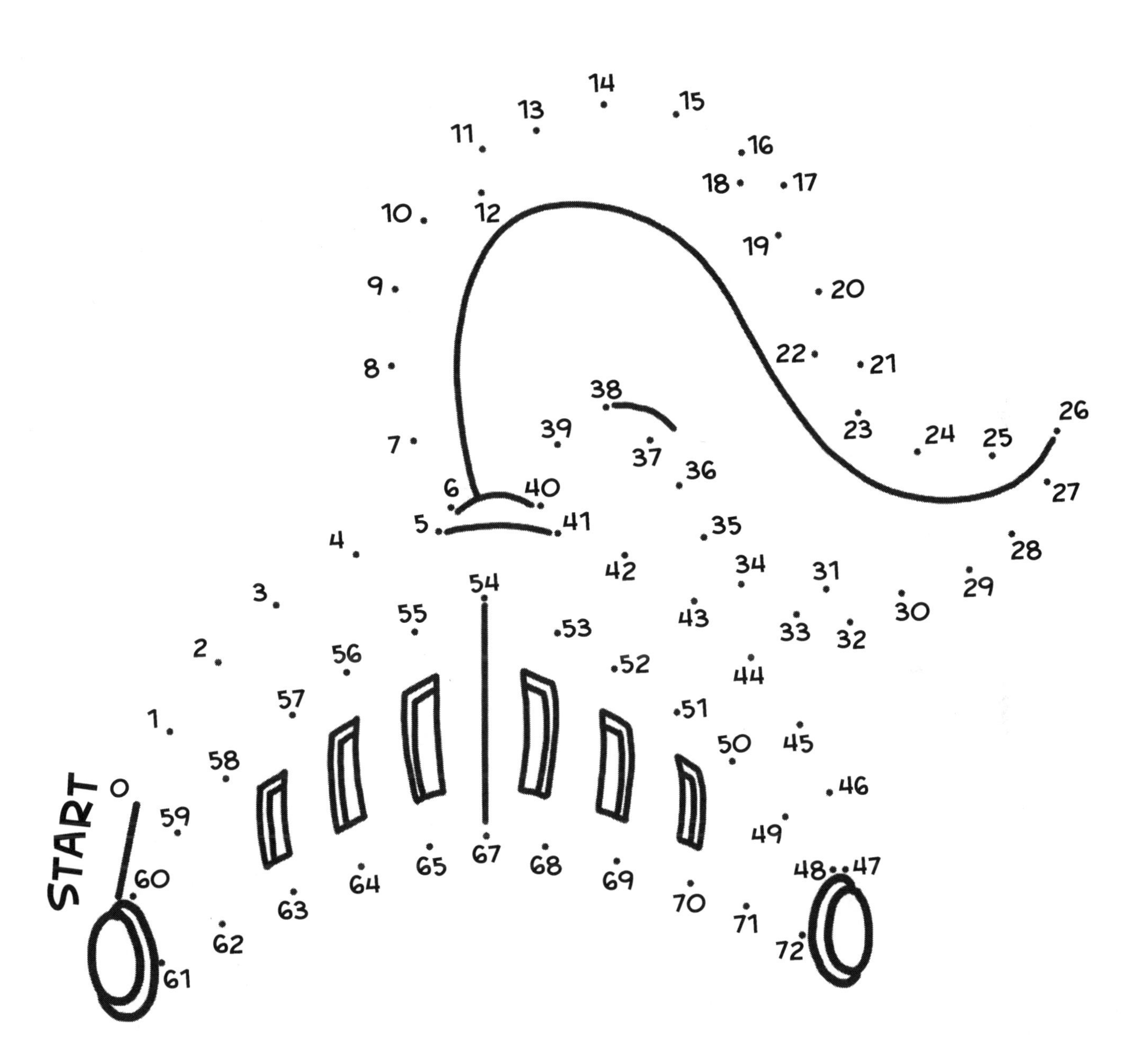

"Take the helmet of salvation."

I can use God's Word as a powerful weapon against the devil. When I'm tempted to do something wrong, the Bible reminds me of what I should do instead.

Start at the sword and follow the path to God's Word.

"And take the sword of the Spirit, which is the Word of God:"

Now that I have my spiritual armor on, I will practice using it. I pray often and ask Jesus to guide me.

Color the speech bubbles that would best match the little girl's prayer from the picture example on the left.

"Always be prayerful and ask God for what you need."

I need to be ready to face the devil at all times and pray that others can do so as well.

Help the little boy on the left picture, to draw his prayers in the boxes below.

"You must always be ready and never give up. Pray often for all of God's people."

(A Prayer:) Dear God, please help me to put on Your armor of the spirit every day. Help me to choose good when I am tempted to do wrong.

Unscramble the words and match them to the armor pieces.

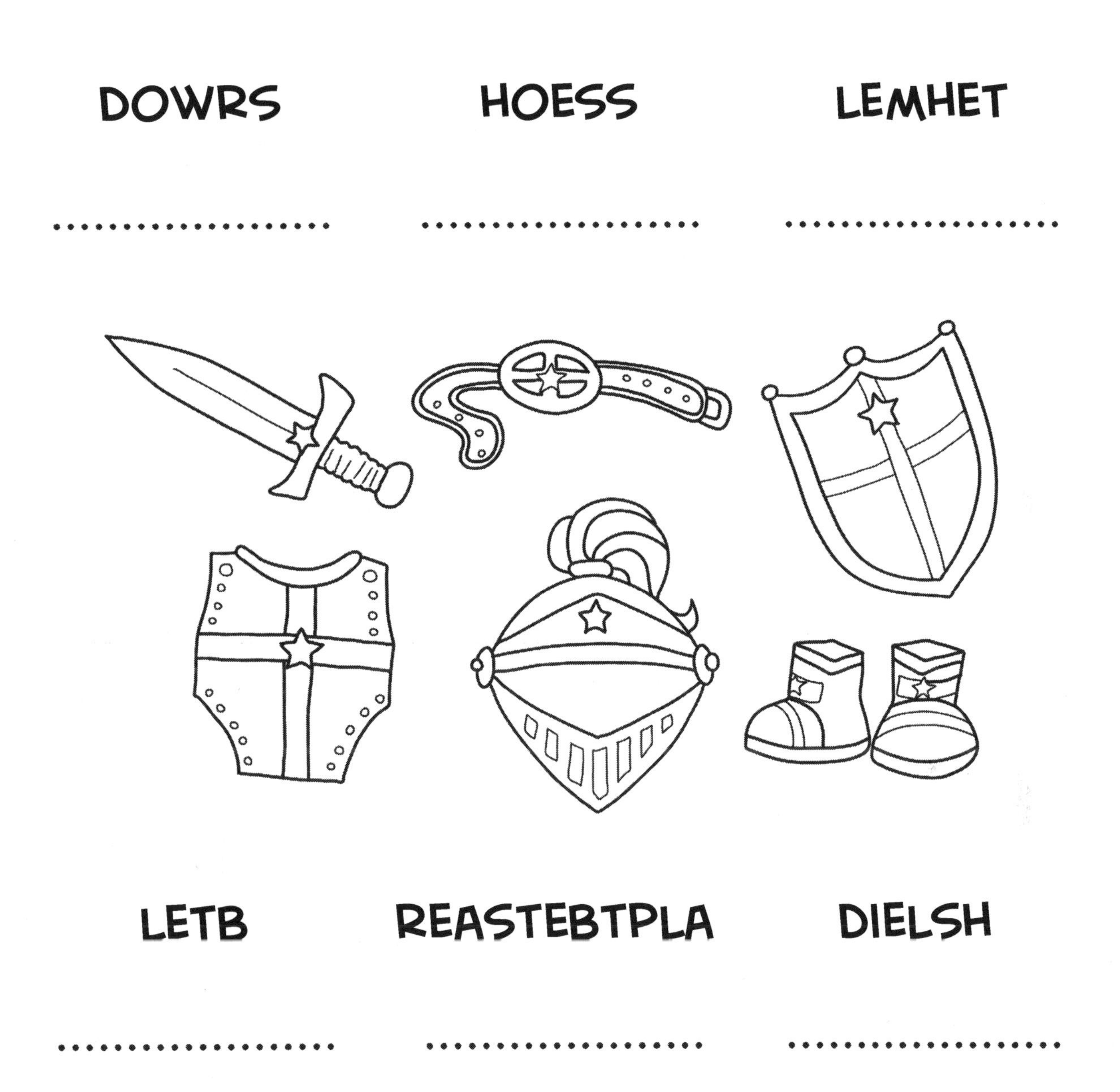

Teach me to do the loving thing. Give me boldness to tell others about You. Remind me to read and follow Your Word. Please make me strong in You. Amen.

(A Praise:) Thank You, dear God, that You have given me this armor of protection against the devil.

Match the shadows to the left picture.

Thank You for giving me strength, even when I feel weak. I praise You for always being there to help me. Amen.

More books from iCharacter

Please help spread the word by introducing your friends to our products.

Visit our website at www.iCharacter.org

Get our books from the iBookstore, B&N, Amazon, Kindle, Google Play and Kobo.

Follow us on Facebook.
www.facebook.com/icharacter

See us on YouTube.
www.youtube.com/icharactervideos

Follow us on Twitter:
@icharacternews

Get FREE downloads

Made in the USA
San Bernardino, CA
05 June 2018